WINDS A'BLOWING

WINDS A'BLOWING

by
MAY JUSTUS

*Illustrated by
Jean Tamburine*

New York   ABINGDON PRESS   *Nashville*

1156235

Many of the poems in this book have appeared in print previously. Acknowledgment is here expressed to the following publishers:

Child Life for "Topsy-Turvy Town," copyright 1955 by May Justus.

Children's Activities for "Apple Tree Hill," "Signs of Christmas," "Lickety-Lick," and "Fairy Ways," copyright 1949, 1951, 1952, 1953, 1959, and 1960 by Child Training Association, Inc.

Jack and Jill for "Fairy Footprints" and "A Sudden Shower," reprinted by special permission from *Jack and Jill*, © 1943, 1956, The Curtis Publishing Company.

Pictures and Stories for "Old Mr. Merryman" and "The Singer," copyright 1941, 1946 by Whitmore and Stone; "The Fairy House" and "Red Shoes," copyright 1947, 1948 by Stone and Pierce; "My Mother's Music," "The Difference," "Trees After Snow," "Spring Secret," and "The Garden Wall," copyright 1949, 1951, 1952 by Pierce and Smith; "When It Rains," "The Boat," and "Merry-Go-Round," copyright 1953, 1956 by Pierce and Washabaugh; "Honey for Sale," copyright 1959 by The Methodist Publishing House.

The Sentinel for "Rose Magic" and "Song for Summer," copyright 1950, 1952 by the Sunday School Board of the Southern Baptist Convention.

Silver Burdett Company for "Sing-Song" from *Music for Early Childhood*, © 1952 by Silver Burdett Company.

Story Parade for "Dishes," "Winds A-Blowing," "Remember September," "Song for Berry Pickers," "Glitter and Gold," "Ballad of a Brownie," "Treasure Hunting," and "Storm on the Mountain," copyright 1939, 1940, 1947, 1948, 1949, 1952, and 1954 by May Justus.

Trails for Juniors for "A Winter Walk" and "Dandelion Gold," copyright 1946, 1947 by Stone and Pierce.

To VERA

Once more to you, because—
There is no friend like a sister
In calm or stormy weather.
CHRISTINA ROSETTI

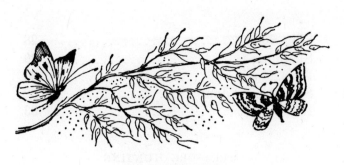

CONTENTS

7

TREASURE HUNTING

ALL AROUND THE YEAR

FAIRY FOOTPRINTS

THREE TIMES AS MANY

Winds A'Blowing

WINDS A'BLOWING

The North Wind is a beggar
  Who shudders at the cold.
The South Wind is a sailor
  With pockets full of gold.
The East Wind is a gypsy
  With saucy cap and feather.
The West Wind is a wizard
  Who conjures wicked weather.

The Winter Wind's a giant
  As grumpy as a bear.
The Summer Wind's a lady
  With flowers in her hair.
The Autumn Wind's an old man
  As touchy as a thistle.
The Spring Wind's a gay lad
  Who blows a silver whistle.

WHEN IT RAINS

"Quack, quack, quack!" says the little white duck.
"Here comes the rain—and I'm in luck.
I don't have to bother with overshoes,
I can splash in the puddles where I choose."

"Oink, oink, oink!" squeals the little red pig.
"Now there'll be plenty of mud to dig.
A fine pig-wallow I'd like to see,
If it rains all day, it will just suit me."

"Boom, boom, boom!" says the big green frog.
"There's no better home than a nice wet bog.
It takes rainy weather to keep it cool
And fill my favorite diving pool."

"Rain, rain, rain!" sigh Jackie and Jill
With elbows propped on the window sill.
Then one gives a whoop, and the other a shout,
The sun and a rainbow have both popped out!

THE FOG

I'll tell you what the fog is:
  A giant old and gray,
Who travels up a valley
  And climbs a mountain way.

He wears about his shoulders
  A gray and ancient cloak,
And carries with him always
  The pipe he likes to smoke.

Why does he climb the mountain,
  Is it for work or fun?
He goes to meet his brother—
  The early morning sun!

A WINTER WALK

There's a path which we can follow
Up a hill and down a hollow.

There's a place I like to go
When the woods are deep with snow.

There's a place I always stop
Underneath a tree-tent top.

At the bottom of the hill
All the winter winds are still.

14

If we wait without a word,
We may glimpse a gallant bird.

Once I saw a curious mouse
Stealing from his hidden house.

Once I saw a startled hare
So surprised, he stopped to stare.

All that we shall hear and see
Waits for us, a mystery!

Come, let's take this path and follow
Up the hill and down the hollow.

THE RAIN HAS SILVER SANDALS

The rain has silver sandals
For dancing in the spring,
And shoes with golden tassels
For summer's frolicking.
Her winter boots have hobnails
Of ice from heel to toe,
Which now and then she changes
For moccasins of snow.

TREES AFTER SNOW

The peach tree wears a picture hat
With dignity and grace;
The pear tree holds a parasol
Of ivory and lace.

The plum tree has a fleecy cloak
To keep her from the cold;
The apple tree beneath her shawl
Looks wrinkled, bent and old.

THE GARDEN WALL

The hollyhocks are very tall.
They look beyond the garden wall;
They see the folk who walk and ride
Along the street that runs outside.

The pansies in their cozy nook
At little neighbor people look,
The things that creep, the things that
   crawl,
Who live on this side of the wall.

Outside the big, high garden gate
The street and all the people wait,
Till I grow big, till I grow tall
And go beyond the garden wall.

I Always Think
of Lovely Things

MY MOTHER'S MUSIC

Whenever Mother plays or sings,
I always think of lovely things.

I like the little tune that goes
As faint and fleet as fairy toes.

One chorus is as clear and sweet
As children laughing in the street.

A merry madcap march she plays
That's like the fun of holidays.

And there's another quick and spry
That sounds like soldiers going by.

In one piece I have always heard
The singing of a happy bird.

Whenever Mother plays or sings,
I always think of lovely things.

PRECIOUS THINGS

Mother has a diamond
   That's like a drop of dew.
Auntie has a sapphire
   That's beautiful and blue.
Sister has a silver chain
   As sweet as it can be;
I've a lovely wishing ring
   I found beneath a tree.
Henry has a singing top,
   Peter has a pup.
Hilda has a dancing doll,
   And Sue a copper cup.
Betty has a money box
   That came across the sea;
I've a lovely secret song
   A fairy gave to me.

FRIENDS

In the morning bright and cool,
That's the time I start for school.

Halfway there, or just about,
Freddie, my best friend, comes out.

If he is a little late,
Then I whistle at his gate.

Down the road we run to try
Who's the fastest, he or I.

When we play a choosing game,
Freddie always calls my name.

I've a knife that's nearly new—
Freddie gets to use it, too.

We are friends, and so we share
Everything, most everywhere.

RED SHOES

My Sunday shoes are shiny black;
　My weekday shoes are brown;
My second-best I wear to school;
　My very best to town.
But oh, how I should like to have
　A pair of new red shoes,
That I could put on any time
　And wear just when I choose.

Now one may walk in shiny black,
　And run in sturdy brown,
But red shoes are the proper kind
　For dancing up and down.
My piggy bank is getting fat
　Upon the corner shelf;
Someday I'll buy those new red shoes,
　And pay for them myself!

THE DIFFERENCE

The rabbit has a habit
Of going in a hurry—
He's off and out of sight with just one bound!
It takes a longer while
For us to walk a mile,
But we have a chance to look around.

GLITTER AND GOLD

Oh, Madam Rain has silver rings,
   And Lady Sun's are gold,
While both have strings of diamonds
   Most dazzling to behold.
And oh, if I were Madam Rain,
   If I were Lady Sun,
I'd give a jewel to a child
   Who doesn't have a one.

THE MOON

Some say it is a ball of gold,
   Some say a piece of cheese;
I don't believe the lovely moon
   Is either one of these.
I think it is a mirror set
   Upon a shining shelf,
Where any little star who likes
   May look and see herself.

THE SINGER

Oh, bluebird in the apple tree,
I like the song you sing to me.
If you will only stay,
I'll sing a song for *you*—oh, dear,
Perhaps he didn't wish to hear—
How fast he flew away!

APPLE TREE HILL

I remember it, yes,
I remember it still.
My Grandmother's cabin
On Apple Tree Hill.
A lean-to behind it,
A walk-way before,
With apple trees shading
The cabin's front door.
An orchard encircled
The neat little yard.
Two apple trees stood
At the gate like a guard.
Through many a winter,
Through many a storm,
An applewood fire
Kept the wee cabin warm.
The hearthstone was deep,
The fireplace wide,
With cracks here and there
Where the crickets could hide.
When shadows came early,
When supper came soon,
We ate apple pie
To a crickety tune.

And sometimes at night,
In the firelight gay,
A lone cricket fiddler
Would tune up to play.
The fire burned down,
And the light would grow dim,
While I munched an apple
And listened to him.
I listened and nodded,
Till the fire burned low,
And Granny cried "Bedtime!"
Then off I would go.
On the floor of the loft room
The apples were spread
Like a lovely bright coverlet,
Yellow and red.
Deep in a featherbed,
All the night long,
I'd dream about apples
And gay cricket song.

I wish, oh, I wish,
I could visit it still,
My Grandmother's cabin
On Apple Tree Hill!

CATERPILLAR DREAM

A caterpillar sound asleep was curled
    upon a limb.
I slipped off very quietly, lest I should
    bother him.
How sad to be awakened by a careless
    passer-by,
If he were dreaming of the day he'd be
    a butterfly!

SING-SONG

Some like a story, some like a song,
Some go a-dancing, some plod along.
Some sing for silver, some sing for bread,
I sing to let the tunes out of my head.

Some like the country, some like the town,
Some travel uphill, some travel down.
Bankers have money, paupers have none,
I have a penny and plenty of fun.

SHOPPING

One day I went to town
  With money in my pocket
I thought I'd buy a golden ring
  Or else a silver locket.

But this is what I brought home—
Explain it if you can!

A man that's made of gingerbread,
  A dancing top that plays a tune,
A candy cane, a yellow ribbon,
  And best of all, a pink balloon!

ROSE MAGIC

I wove myself a rosebud crown
And pinned rose petals to my gown.

A rainpool mirror let me see
A smiling face look up at me.

And what a change had come to pass—
What magic in that looking-glass!

The crown that sat upon my hair
Was one a fairy queen might wear.

30

The faded old blue gingham dress
Was now a robe of loveliness.

Could this be—could this be true?
Inside the gate I fairly flew.

I ran inside, I rushed upstairs,
I bumped the bedpost and the chairs.

Then in a mirror on a shelf
I saw my ordinary self.

The crown was lost, its glory gone,
I had the same old blue dress on.

Only one thing kept its place;
The smile that lingered on my face.

STRAWBERRY JAM

I went visiting Miss Melinda,
  Miss Melinda Brown.
She has a cottage in the country;
  I live here in town.

"Guess what I've got for dinner, dearie,"
  Miss Melinda said.
"Strawberry jam"—(my nose had guessed it!)
  "Strawberry jam—and bread."

Strawberry jam in the corner cupboard,
  On the middle shelf.
She let me stand on a chair and tip-toe—
  Get it down myself.

Somehow, visiting Miss Melinda,
  Time goes by on wings.
"What do you do all alone?" I asked her.
  "I make jam and things."

When it was time to go home, I kissed her,
  "Thanks for the lovely day!"
"Thank you for coming," said Miss Melinda.
  "Come again right away!"

DISHES

Applesauce is sweeter in a bowl that's
    white and pink.
Bread and milk is nicer in a blue one,
    so I think,
Any food is flavored by the twinkle
    in the spoon.
Yes, there *is* a difference, you'll find it
    very soon.
Even if you're hungry, and your dinner's
    rather late
Bread and butter's better if it's on a flowered
    plate.
Prunes are very plain, I know, but oh, how much
    I wish
Every child could eat them from a shining
    yellow dish.

Treasure Hunting

TREASURE HUNTING

"Look!" said Tommy,
"Look!" cried he.
"See what I've found—
This funny old key!"
A funny old key,
Buried in the sand.
Dropped, maybe,
From a pirate's hand.
Dropped from his hand
On the very day
He was hiding,
His gold away.
While he was hiding
His gold in a box—
This was the key
To the big brass locks.

"Listen," said Tommy,
"Listen," said he,
"Let's find the treasure
  Buried by the sea.
  Half will be mine,
  Half will go to you."
"Yes," I agreed.
"That's the thing to do."
  When Tommy goes treasure hunting
  I go, too.

JESSICA JANE

Jessica Jane is the kind of cook
Who doesn't need a recipe book.
Little trouble indeed she takes
When she makes puddings and pies and cakes.
With a twist of her wrist and a pat-a-pat
She turns them out in a row—like that!
There in a row in the summer sun
They bake and bake till they're all well done.
Grocery problems are not for her—
She has plenty of mud and a stick to stir.

OLD MR. MERRYMAN

Old Mr. Merryman lives down the lane,
Walks all around with his gold-headed cane,
Gives all the children his friendliest smile,
Lets them sit down on his step for awhile.

Old Mr. Merryman showed me one day
All the fine clothes that he has put away:
Scarlet and yellow, with buttons of gold,
He was a gay man before he grew old.

Old Mr. Merryman, once was a clown,
That's what they tell of him here in the town.
One day I asked him, and guess what he said?
"Look at me, will you?", and stood on his head!

Old Mr. Merryman sporty and spry
Waves to the folk who go hurrying by,
Old people, young people, women and men—
Only the children will stop now and then.

WHISTLE, BOY, WHISTLE

Dim trail winding through the dusky hollow,
Long, lone journey for a lad to follow.
No one for company but Old Man Moon—
Whistle, boy, whistle up a blithe, bold tune!

One mile gets you over Humpback Hill—
(That was nothing but a whippoorwill.)
Dare the boogers as you brogue along,
Whistle, boy, whistle up a sassy song!

Next mile takes you over Bare Bone Creek—
(That was nothing but a hoot owl's shriek.)
Step a little faster, sonny, just don't run.
Whistle, boy, whistle something, just for fun!

Last mile finds you at the pasture pond.
Home place is waiting just a jump beyond.
Home light is shining through the orchard trees—
Whistle, boy, whistle any tune you please!

HONEY FOR SALE

Folks can't remember when Uncle Billy Blair
Didn't peddle honey in Courthouse Square,
Every warm Saturday, when the weather's fair,

"Buy, buy, buy a pot of apple-blossom honey!
Only a dollar each and worth the money."

High on the mountain among his apple trees
Lives Uncle Billy and all his honeybees.
"Fine place to live," he says. "Do as I please."

He makes the honey pots, the bees make the honey.
Only a dollar each, and well worth the money.

Come, I will take you to Uncle Billy Blair,
When he peddles honey in Courthouse Square,
This very next Saturday, if the weather's fair.

We'll buy a pot or two of apple-blossom honey.
Only a dollar each, and well worth the money.

DAVY CROCKETT'S POCKETS

They say that Davy Crockett
   had a secret pocket,
And in this secret pocket
   he kept a hidden charm.
It looked like a funny
   piece of old money,
It was supposed to bring him luck
   And keep him safe from harm.

They say that Davy Crockett
   had another pocket,
And in this other pocket
   were ordinary things:
Bullets spic-and spandy,
   A knife always handy,
He took along for extra luck
   on all his journeyings.

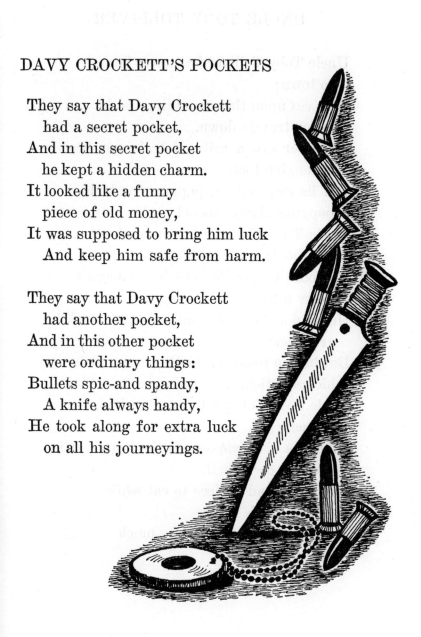

UNCLE TOBY TOLLIVER

Uncle Toby Tolliver has never been
  to town;
He lives upon the mountain, and he
  never travels down.
He never saw a railroad train nor heard
  an engine toot,
But he can make a popgun—and his
  popguns always shoot!
Uncle Toby Tolliver has never been
  to school;
He doesn't know his ABC's; he doesn't
  know a rule.
He cannot name the continents nor work
  arithmetic,
But he can make a whistle from a little
  hickory stick.
Uncle Toby Tolliver lives only with
  himself;
He bakes his cornpone on the hearth and
  keeps it on a shelf.
One day I had a piece to eat while
  sitting by his fire—
Uncle Toby is a man I very much
  admire.

BRIGHT AND BEAUTIFUL

Up in the attic I found some hidden treasure,
  Three bright jewels in a cranny of the floor.
Lost for a long time, a long time, no telling—
  Maybe, maybe even a hundred years or more.

One little bead is as red as any ruby;
  One is a beautiful sapphire blue.
The third one really isn't any kind of color,
  But oh, how it twinkles when the light shines through!

The red bead I sewed on a ribbon for a necklace;
  The blue bead I tied on a thread to make a ring.
The other one I'm keeping for a charm in my pocket—
  For oh, when it twinkles, it's a magic thing!

All Around the Year

IN WINTER'S WALL

The house of Old Man Winter
   Seems dull and dreary gray,
Till sometimes of a sudden
   Will come a sunny day.
Then from a casement window
   Set in a somber wall
He leans to glimpse the springtime
   And hear a bluebird's call.

MARCH TO APRIL

Said March to Miss April, "I'm glad you are here
To finish the work I have started this year,
Though much has been done, there is much still to do,
Which I am now leaving, Miss April, to you.

"The floor of the earth is already swept clean,
Awaiting your carpet of velvety green.
In hollows and hedges I've melted the snow,
Where you can make bluebells and buttercups grow.

"A dear little crocus is lingering on—
Let somebody find it before it is gone!
And tell that narcissus asleep by the gate
To wake up and jump up before it's too late.

DANDELION GOLD

Old Man Winter
　　Left in such a hurry
He dropped a pocketful of gold
　　That flew off in a flurry.

Perhaps he didn't miss it—
　　Perhaps he didn't mind;
But now it's free for you and me
　　And anyone to find.

THE DRESS OF SPRING

When Spring came tiptoe up the hill,
　　Her green-gold dress was made
From a web March spun on a wheel of sun,
　　And wove on a loom of shade.

When Spring went dancing down the hill,
　　Her dress was a May Day dream—
With ruffles of showers and April flowers,
　　All stitched with a rainbow seam.

SPRING SECRET

Nobody knows what I know—
   Nobody knows but me!
I hunted around and around about
To find the secret, and found it out.
Nobody knows what I know,
   Nobody knows but me!

Nobody knows what I know,
   Nobody knows but me!
It's high-up-high in an apple tree,
And snug and safe as a nest can be.
Nobody knows what we know—
   The Mother bird and me!

SIGNS OF SPRING

I know, I know, I know it—
  The Spring is here at last.
There's dogwood on the hillside,
  And redbud coming fast.
Wake robin's in the deep woods,
  And wild geranium,
I know, I know, I know it—
  The lovely Spring has come!

49

SUDDEN SHOWER

Mr. Weatherman one day was walking
    through the sky;
Down below he saw the earth was dusty,
    hot, and dry.
"On a day like this," he said, "those people
    must be hot.
They would like a shower from my biggest
    water-pot."
But alas, alackaday, for Mr. Weatherman
Stumbled on a thunder-cloud and
    dropped his water can.
Crash! Splash! And everyone went running
    for his door.
"Such a rain as this," they said, "we've
    never seen before!"

SUMMER STORM

Flash! goes the lightning's zig-zag signal,
Crash! goes the thunder's big bass drum.
Splash! come the raindrops,
    Dash! come the children,
    Hurrying, scurrying, headed for home!

SONG FOR SUMMER

June makes the tune
  Of Summer's sweetest song.
Soon, soon she teaches it
  To all who come along.
A thrush in a bush;
  "Lirra—lirra—ling!"
A cricket in a thicket:
  "Zing—zing—zing!"
A frog in a bog:
  "Boom—boom—boom!"
A bee in a blossom:
  "Zoom—zoom—zoom!"
Listen—listen!
  There's music all about.
Does anybody want to sing
  Or whistle—or shout?

REMEMBER SEPTEMBER

Remember September;
   Before she said good-by,
She told the youngest robins
   The way they ought to fly.
Around the mountain's shoulder
   She spread a gypsy shawl,
And sent a breeze among the trees
   To sing about the Fall.

Remember September;
   Before she went away
She taught the cricket fiddlers
   The proper tunes to play.
She gave a modest maple
   A dress of red and gold,
And showed a mouse a little house
   To keep him through the cold.

JACK FROST

I met Jack Frost this morning,
    And he was feeling blue.
"I wish to goodness," said he,
    "You'd tell me what to do.
The house of Mr. Squirrel
    I painted gold and red.
And now he doesn't like it—
    He wants it green instead!"

LUCK FOR HALLOWEEN

It was a wise old woman
 Who gave this charm to me.
It works the best on Halloween—
 Or so said she!
"Find a four-leaf clover,
 Wear it in your shoe,
Right foot, left foot,
 Either one will do.
It will lead you into luck
 Before the day is through."

So find a four-leaf clover,
 And put it to the test.
It *might* work anytime—
 But Halloween is best!

STORM ON THE MOUNTAIN

The storm around our cabin like a wild beast howled.
It leaped upon the roof and down the chimney growled.
We children in the corners, with our hands upon our
ears,
Were trying hard to hush our cries and blink away the
tears.
Then out spoke our father, "This will never do at all!"
He jumped up and took down his fiddle from the wall.
He tuned it in a jiffy, then he started on a jig—
And all at once the Thing outside didn't seem so big!
Soon our hands were clapping to "The Golden Willow
Tree,"
And our feet were tapping to "A Pretty Sight to See."
The music was so merry and our laughter was so gay
That no one, no one, noticed when the wild storm slunk
away!

WHEN THE WIND LAUGHED

The Old wind laughed as he passed our door—
A laugh I never had heard before.
He cried, "Ha! Ha!" and he cried, "Ho! Ho!
I know something that *you* don't know!"

"Tell me, oh tell me, Mr. Wind," said I.
But he laughed at me, and he went on by.

The Old Wind laughed in the chimney place,
And wouldn't come down to show his face.
He cried, "Ha! Ha!" and he cried, "Ho! Ho!
I know something that *you* don't know!"

"Tell me, oh tell me, Mr. Wind," said I.
But he only laughed as he went on by.

The Old Wind whistled: "Look out! Look out!"
Then I ran outside, and I looked about—
And caught my breath! For the air was thick
With feathers out of the sky's bedtick.

"And how did you know, Mr. Wind?" said I.
But he laughed and laughed, and he went on by.

SIGNS OF CHRISTMAS

Dancing, prancing
Here and there,
Round a corner,
Up a stair,
Through a doorway,
Down a street—
Hurry, scurry,
Go the feet.
Hustling, bustling
In and out,
Folks go gaily
All about.
From the signs
We see and hear,
Christmas time
Is very near!

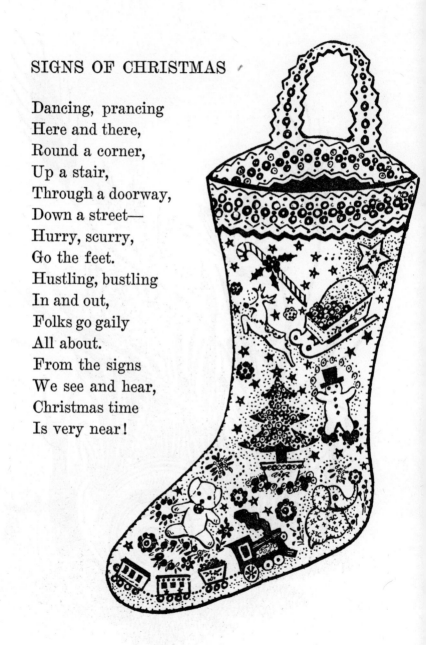

Fairy Footprints

FAIRY FOOTPRINTS

A path runs through the orchard grass,
　A crooked little trail;
And no one ever seems to pass
　But one old pokey snail.
Still there are tiny footprints there—
　And I can tell you whose:
I'd recognize them anywhere—
　They're made by pointed shoes!

I HEARD THE FAIRIES

I heard the fairies singing,
   I'm sure as sure can be!
The garden gate was swinging,
   And I ran in to see.
But suddenly they vanished,
And all I saw, alack!
Was one wee cricket fiddler
   Retreating through a crack.

THE FAIRY HOUSE

I've found a fairy house at last—I found it yesterday.
I found it in a little wood where I had gone to play.
I found it by a winding path which led me to the door,
And none, I'm sure, but fairy folk had traveled it before.

Outside it's just exactly like a very old oak tree,
But, oh, the door was open, and I couldn't help but see
The little mushroom tables and the little toadstool chairs,
And such a funny little step that led away upstairs.

A mossy rug was on the floor, so very smooth and neat.
I looked and looked and thought I saw the print of fairy
    feet.
A hammock made of spider lace was swinging to and fro,
To rock the fairy babies in at sleepy time, you know.

I hadn't been invited, so of course I couldn't stay.
Besides the little fairy folk all chanced to be away.
And so I kissed a clover leaf and hung it on the wall,
To tell the fairy family that I had been to call.

BALLAD OF A BROWNIE

When Granny was a little lass, she lived beyond the sea
In Donalderry Village, by the river Donaldee.
And this is when and this is where that Granny came to
  know
A little man, a brownie man, who lived there long ago.

One day the cows had wandered far beyond the pasture
  gate,
And Granny had to look them up, though it was growing
  late.
She hunted for them everywhere, but not a one could
  find,
Then here they came across the hill, the brownie man
  behind!

The brownie man could put a patch upon a ragged shoe;
He did it once for Granny when her toes were sticking
  through.
He did it by the firelight after she had gone to bed—
The best job he had ever seen, the village cobbler said.

And one day when the bin was bare and want was at the
  door,
She swept the house and found a coin upon the wooden
  floor.
So bright it was, so beautiful, it made the folks all stare,
And Granny knew the brownie man had been to put it
  there.

"You must have been a lucky lass," I said to her one day.
"Nobody ever helps *me* out in this surprising way."
"You never lived," said Granny, as she smiled and
  winked at me,
"In Donalderry Village, by the river Donaldee."

FLITTER-MIDGE

The bees and butterflies, they say
   Are feeling rather blue,
For little Fairy Flitter-Midge
   Is drinking up the dew.
She visits every posy patch,
   Each open flower cup,
And should there be a drop inside,
   She's sure to drink it up.

The bees and butterflies are cross,
   And I can tell you why.
The honey pots in flower land
   Are getting very dry.
For little Fairy Flitter-Midge
   Has been to every one
And left them hanging upside down
   To show what she has done!

FAIRY WAYS

The fairies have houses, but few ever find them;
  The door is a cranny or crack in the wall,
With never a hint of the wee folk behind them,
  And people who pass never notice at all.

The ways of the fairy folk cause me to wonder:
  Do you think when a fairy wishes to hide,
She spreads out her ruffles and ducks her head under,
  And looks like a flower to those alongside?

The fairies have tricks that are certainly clever,
  An elfin-sweet song I have many times heard,
But though I looked quick as a wink, I could never
  See anything there but a little brown bird.

The way to the land of the fairies is hidden.
  The gate is a bramble, the latch is a rose.
Nobody can enter unless he is bidden,
  And he cannot tell you the way that he goes.

FAIRY JEWELS

The fairies hide their jewels at the bottom of the brook,
  And oh, but they are beautiful, all yellow, green and
    gold!
But should a body pick them up to take a better look,
  He'll find no jewels in his hand, but pebbles pale and
    cold.

The fairies hang their jewels on the branches of the trees,
  And oh, but they are fine to see, all yellow, green and
    red!
But should a body shake a branch to gather what he sees,
  He'll get no jewels for his crown—but showers for his
    head!

MISER MUCKLE

Miser Muckle was an elf;
  In a hill he had a house
He had purchased for himself
  From a certain Mr. Mouse.
And it suited to a T
  All his purposes he found.
Miser Muckle worked, you see,
  With his treasures underground.

Oh, the happy days he spent
  Making money out of gold,
Till his little back grew bent,
  And his little heart grew cold.
When a beggar passing by
  Craved a coin from out his store,
"Not a penny!" he would cry
  As he turned him from the door.

When the tale at last was told
  To the queen upon the throne—
All about the hidden gold
  And the elf who lived alone—
"This will never do!" she cried.

"Tell the Miser that I say
If he keeps his foolish pride,
  He'll regret it some fine day."

When the elf-man got this word,
  Loud he laughed in impish glee—
Laughed as if he had not heard.
  "Go," he cried, "don't bother me!"
On them all he turned his back
  And began to work again.
Said the messengers: "Alack!
  All we say is just in vain."

Then a strange thing came to pass
  In the little home below.
Now the Miser cried, "Alas!"
  For his gold began to grow.
Up it grew so very fast,
  Up it grew without a sound.
Until every piece at last
  Lay bright yellow on the ground.

"Look!" the children cried next day,
  "See the dandelions here!
See how many! See how large—
  They're the first ones of the year!"

Miser Muckle sat alone
  Saying, "Oh, alas! Alack!"
For his greedy gold was gone,
  And he could not get it back.

Three Times as Many

LUCKY PENNY

If you should earn a penny,
　How lucky that would be!
And though you have not any
　To keep it company,
It's luck if you will take it
　And carry it along,
And in your pocket shake it,
　And sing this little song:

Ho, for a lucky penny!
It's better than not any.
Hey, diddle-dee! what luck for me.
To earn two times as many!

Now you may think it funny,
　What I am telling you,
But keep your lucky money,
　Till there are pennies two.

Then when their jingle-jingle
  Is like a little song,
Take up this dee-dum-dingle,
  And sing it loud and long:

Ho, for a lucky penny!
It's better than not any.
Hey, diddle-dee! I'll soon have three,
And soon three times as many!

THE BOAT

This morning as I went to school
I passed along a little pool
To watch a boat without an oar
Go sailing to the farther shore.

What fun, I thought, to take a ride
And see what's on the other side.
But this I could not do at all—
The little leaf boat was too small!

SONG FOR BERRY PICKERS

Shining buckets, all a-swing—
Hear their music, jingle-jing!
We are going berrying.

Down the lane a mile or so,
There's a berry patch we know
That we found there long ago.

There are vines like fairy trees
Beckoning with every breeze:
"Here is treasure—take it, please!"

Who is nimble, who is quick?
Who is first to find and pick
Where the berries cluster thick?

Rattle, rattle! Hear them drop
In the bucket! Never stop
Till the berries reach the top!

Buckets full and heaping high—
We shall have blackberry pie
For our dinner by and by.

GRANDMOTHER'S TEAKETTLE

Grandmother's teakettle swings on a crane
Crooning a ditty again and again;
Never a-weary, nor seeming to tire,
Grandmother's teakettle sings to the fire;
  "Boil away, boil away, boil away me!
    Homefolks are waiting and wanting their tea."

Grandmother's teakettle homely and stout,
Laughs with the funniest sputter and spout.
Nothing amusing at all do I see.
What is it, teakettle, tell it to me.
  "Laugh away, laugh away, little girl, do!
    Tea time is coming, is coming for you."

Grandmother's teakettle swung long ago,
Singing that same little song clear and low.
Grandmother knows just as well as I do
What the old teakettle is singing of, too.
  "Sing away, swing away, chuckle along,
    Just the same teakettle, just the same song."

MERRY-GO-ROUND

The merry-go-round is lovely,
   The merry-go-round is gay;
Whenever I ride
     on the merry-go-round,
   I wish I could ride all day.

I wish I could ride forever
   In time to the twinkling tune.
The only thing wrong
     with a merry-go-round,
   It comes to a stop too soon.

PUSSYCAT

It takes a little of this and that
To make the right kind of pussycat.

A set of whiskers, a well-washed face,
A tail to wave in its proper place.

Four paws well-cushioned against the cold,
With claws kept safe in their hidden hold.

A suit of britches and coat in one
To wear him well in the rain and sun.

A mannerly mew and a happy purr
To say "Please, Ma'am" or "Thank you, Sir!"

And somewhere inside a cat's wise heart
To know his friend and his foe apart.

It takes all this, it takes all that
To make the right kind of pussycat.

KINDS OF TALK

Most people need a lot of words;
　　They chirp and chatter like the birds,
While Dog's bow-wow and Pussy's mew—
　　Say everything they wish to you.

POKER AND TONGS

The Poker is a quiet man, perhaps a bit severe,
Who punches up the lazy fire, and says, "Get busy here!"

Then Tinker Tongs comes after him, a smile upon his
　　face,
Picks up a most discouraged stick, and puts him into
　　place.

LICKETY-LICK

Lickety, lickety, lickety-lick!
The frosting is getting all thickety-thick—
The beautiful frosting
That Mother will take
To trim up the wonderful
Company cake!
But some of the sweet stuff
Is certain to stick
To the bowl and the spoon.
Judy, Johnny, come quick;
Here's the bowl,
Here's the spoon,
For a lickety-lick!

TOPSY-TURVY TOWN

If you lived in Topsy-turvy Town,
You'd walk in a circle upside down.
You'd wear your clothes all inside out,
And even your shoes would go round-about!
The honey is sour, and the vinegar sweet,
The bunnies are slow, the turtles are fleet.
The snow is black, the ink is white,
The sun is gray and the shadows bright.
The rain is dusty, the dew is dry,
The trees grow low, and the people, high.
The ice is hot, and the fires are cold,
Grandpas are young, and babies old.
The roses are green, and grass is red,
Folks get up there when we go to bed.
Sad people laugh and glad ones frown,
In the place called Topsy-turvy Town!

ADVENTURE

One night a little firefly
  Was looking at a star,
And said—though no one heard him—
  "I wonder what you are!"
Then, eager for adventure,
  And brave as he could be,
He trimmed his tiny lantern
  And flew away to see!